CAST OF CHARACTERS

TROJANS: people from Troy

GREEKS: people from Greece

HELEN: beautiful Spartan queen who fell in love with Paris

MENELAUS: king of Sparta and husband of Helen

PARIS: Trojan prince who fell in love with Helen

AGAMEMNON: Greek king and brother to Menelaus

ODYSSEUS: Greek king and the mastermind behind the Trojan Horse

EPEUS: friend of Odysseus, and the builder of the Trojan horse

ATHENA: goddess of war and wisdom

SINON: Greek soldier who tricked the Trojans into accepting the Trojan Horse as a gift

LAOCOÖN: Trojan man who warned that the Trojan horse was a trick

WORDS TO KNOW

OFFERING something that is presented as a gift

SACRED something holy, usually connected with religion

SPARTA ancient Greek city-state

TEMPLE building used for worship

TROJAN WAR mythological ten-year battle between the people of Troy and Greece. The war began when Helen left her Greek husband Menelaus for the Trojan Paris.

TROY ancient city believed to have existed in present-day Turkey

THOUSANDS OF YEARS AGO,

the Trojans and Greeks fought a war over a beautiful woman named Helen. Helen was married to Menelaus, the king of Sparta, in Greece.

A Trojan prince named Paris fell in love with Helen. She could not resist Paris' handsome face and romantic ways. She, too, fell deeply in love. Secretly, the two of them sailed away together to Troy.

Menelaus was furious at Paris for stealing his wife. He sought revenge. Menelaus asked his brother, King Agamemnon, for help. Agamemnon gathered a thousand Greek ships full of the best soldiers and sailed for Troy.

When the ships arrived on Troy's shores, they encountered a problem. Troy was a walled city. The soldiers could not get into the city to find Helen. Instead, the Greeks and Trojans fought battle after battle on the beaches surrounding Troy.

The battles became known as the Trojan War. The war raged on for ten years. Many people died, but the Greeks still had not been able to get into the city to find Helen. Then, Odysseus came up with a clever plan.

It had been another long day of fighting, and the smell of blood still hung in the air.

Odysseus wiped the sweat from his forehead. "When will this war end?" he wondered as he removed his armour. "We can't go on this way," he said to himself. "We need to try something new – something clever that will trick the Trojans into letting us into their city."

Odysseus changed his clothes and bandaged his wounds. Then he went out to the fire to see which of his friends had survived another day.

Odysseus found his friend Epeus by the fire. Epeus was carving a small wooden horse.

"The moon is full tonight," said Epeus. "My daughter is probably out riding her horse in the moonlight. We used to ride together, before the war."

Epeus worked on the horse's mane as Odysseus watched the sparks from the fire dart back and forth.

"It's finished," said Epeus. "It will make a nice birthday gift for my daughter."

Epeus held up the wooden horse so that Odysseus could take a closer look. "There's a secret compartment in the horse's belly," he said. "I'm going to put a gold coin inside as a surprise."

Epeus paused. "Odysseus," he said, "the gods seem to favour you. If I die in this war, will you make sure my daughter gets this gift?"

Odysseus put his hand on Epeus' shoulder. So many of his friends had already died. "Of course I will, Epeus," he said.

That night, with the goddess Athena's help, Odysseus had a dream – a dream that would help end the Trojan War.

Odysseus dreamt of Epeus' wooden horse. However, this wooden horse could not fit into any saddlebag. It was enormous! It stood at the height of ten men. In the horse's belly was a trapdoor, just like the compartment in Epeus' little horse.

In his dream, Odysseus went up through the trapdoor and into the horse's belly. It smelled of clean, fresh wood. Inside, there were several benches. Each had a man's name carved on to it. Odysseus read the names just as he began to wake up.

EPEUS

PHILOCTETES

NEOPTOLEMUS

ODYSSEUS

DIOMEDES

9

Odysseus spent the next day excitedly drawing plans for a giant wooden horse.

When he had finished, Odysseus went in search of King Agamemnon. He found him in his tent.

"Agamemnon," said Odysseus, "I had a dream. I think Athena must have sent it to me. I believe I have thought of a way to end the war."

Agamemnon raised his eyebrow. "Will it help us get inside the walled city?" he asked. "This war won't end until we capture Helen."

Odysseus nodded. "I believe it will."

Odysseus left Agamemnon's tent with a smile. He went right to Epeus' tent.

"Epeus," said Odysseus, "I have a job for you. I want you to make a horse just like the one you made for your daughter, with a secret compartment in its belly. This time, though, I want you to make a horse that will hold twenty-five men inside."

Epeus looked puzzled.

Odysseus smiled at his friend. "Your gift horse may be our way to end this war!"

Odysseus explained his plan to Epeus. "When we have finished building the horse, we'll pack up camp," he said. "Everyone, except twenty-six men, will board the boats and sail further down the coast, out of sight. Twenty-five of us will climb into the belly of the horse. Sinon will remain on the beach, pretending he has been abandoned.

Sinon will explain to the Trojans that we had finally tired of battle and left for home. He'll say we left the horse as a goodwill offering to Athena. The Trojans will pull the horse into the walled city and place it near Athena's temple.

At night, while the Trojans are sleeping, Sinon will signal to the boats that the horse is inside the city's walls. Then, when our soldiers arrive, we will let them in and take the city by moonlight!"

Epeus began straight away. He collected together the best carpenters and set to work. First, the men needed to gather wood for the horse.

"Where are we going to find that much wood?" Epeus wondered. The beach did not have any large trees. There was only one place they could get wood – from their ships.

The soldiers carefully took apart twenty of their wooden ships. They put all the wood into a large pile.

Epeus smiled. "Good work!" he said. "Now we have enough wood for our gift horse!"

The men worked hard. They measured and cut. They figured and hammered. Soon the giant wooden horse was finished.

It was magnificent!

Odysseus gathered the men whose names he had seen in his dream. They climbed into the belly of the wooden horse. They carefully placed their armour and weapons between cloth and wool. When the horse moved they would be silent. Then they sat down to wait.

"Athena, great goddess of war and wisdom," Odysseus silently prayed, "please bring us victory!"

The rest of the men packed up and sailed away down the coast. Sinon was the only Greek to be seen – Sinon and a large wooden horse. The Trojans watched from the high wall.

"Look!" they shouted. "They're leaving! The war is finally over! But what is that? A horse?"

The Trojans sent out some men to inspect the horse. They found Sinon. "Who are you? What is this?" they asked.

Sinon replied, "My name is Sinon. The Greeks abandoned me. They thought I favoured your side. This horse is a peace offering to Athena."

The Trojans walked around the horse. "We should take it into the city!" they said. "We will put it in Athena's temple."

A Trojan man named Laocoön thought the horse was a trick. "Beware of Greeks bearing gifts," he warned.

Suddenly, two giant snakes emerged from the sea and ate him!

The Trojans decided it was best not to listen to Laocoön.

"It's the will of the gods for us to accept this offering," said the Trojans.

They opened the city gates and wheeled the giant horse into Athena's temple.

Odysseus and his men were finally inside the city. Now, they had to be quiet and wait.

That evening the Trojans had a big party. They were happy the war was over. They ate and drank. They laughed and danced late into the night. Finally, they went home to bed.

When the Trojans were all asleep, Sinon climbed a ladder to the horse's trapdoor and let out the Greek warriors.

Odysseus shook Sinon's hand. "Good work, Sinon! They believed you! Now, hurry to the gate and let in the rest of our soldiers!"

The Greeks set Troy on fire. The sleepy Trojans woke up to smoke and flames. "The city is burning!" they screamed.

The Trojan leaders rallied the men. "Fight for Troy! Save your families!" they cried.

Swords clashed and muscles strained as the bloody battle wore on into the morning.

The Trojans fought bravely, but the Greeks had caught them unawares. The wooden horse had worked. The Greeks had won the war, and the beautiful Helen was returned to Menelaus.

The Greeks took what they wanted from the ruined city. Odysseus' men even robbed Athena's sacred temple. Athena was furious. She cursed Odysseus and his men to suffer for their crime by wandering the seas for ten long years.

Although Odysseus was destined to sail the seas for many years, the gods blew Epeus' ship home with great speed. Epeus was able to present his daughter with the gift horse himself.

"He's lovely, Father!" she said.

Epeus looked up at the sky. "Thank you, Odysseus," he whispered.

www.raintreepublishers.co.uk
Visit our website to find out
more information about
Raintree books.

To order:
☎ Phone 0845 6044371
🖶 Fax +44 (0) 1865 312263
✉ Email myorders@raintreepublishers.co.uk

Customers from outside the UK please telephone +44 1865 312262

Raintree is an imprint of Capstone Global Library Limited, a company incorporated
in England and Wales having its registered office at 7 Pilgrim Street, London, EC4V 6LB
– Registered company number: 6695582

Text © Picture Window Books 2012
First published in the United Kingdom in 2012
The moral rights of the proprietor have been asserted.

We would like to thank Terry Flaherty, Professor of English at
Minnesota State University for his advice and expertise.

Editors: Shelly Lyons and Vaarunika Dharmapala
Designer: Alison Thiele
Art Director: Nathan Gassman
Production Specialist: Sarah Bennett
The illustrations in this book were created with watercolours, gouache, acrylics, and digital technology.

ISBN 978 1 406 24307 9 (paperback)
16 15 14 13 12
10 9 8 7 6 5 4 3 2 1

British Library Cataloguing in Publication Data
A full catalogue record for this book is available from the British Library.